ビッグ・ヒーロー6

Disney
BIG HERO 6

HIRO'S
SAN FRANSOKYO
FILES

PaRRagon

Bath • New York • Cologne • Melbourne • Delhi
Hong Kong • Shenzhen • Singapore • Amsterdam

The bustling city of San Fransokyo is home to the best tech company in the world, Krei Tech, and San Fransokyo Institute of Technology, a leading university.

It is also home to the Hamada brothers, Tadashi and his little brother Hiro, who live with their Aunt Cass above her coffee shop, The Lucky Cat Café.

Tadashi and Hiro are great inventors. Hiro loves to build robots and is excited when he finds out that he could win admission to San Fransokyo Tech.

To help Hiro with his invention, Tadashi takes him to the robotics lab at the university, where Hiro meets Tadashi's favourite robotics professor, Robert Callaghan.

"I need to go to this school...." thinks Hiro as he looks around the lab. He knows that the best way to get in to the Tech is by presenting the best invention ever at the university's Tech Showcase.

To find the best parts for his invention, Hiro and Tadashi
visit junkyards with four of Tadashi's friends.
Honey Lemon loves working with chemicals and taking
selfies with the reactions.

Wasabi is an amazing physics student who uses technology to keep organized.

Go Go Tomago loves mechanical engineering and anything that goes fast!

And then there is Fred. He just loves comics and hanging out with his friends.

Working in the robotics lab at the university, Tadashi creates Baymax, the world's first portable robotic medical aide. Tadashi is excited to introduce a nurse-bot called Baymax to his brother and their friends.

Baymax inflates when someone
is hurt, then goes on to diagnose
and treat patients on the spot.

Baymax's caregiving
nature is programmed
on to a green computer
chip that is plugged
into him. He will only
shut down after his
patient says, "I am
satisfied with my care."

Hiro has worked hard to prepare for the showcase. When it is his turn, Hiro makes a huge impact with his tiny robots called microbots.

He has created thousands of these robots that link together.

"The microbots are controlled with this neural transmitter," Hiro tells the audience as he points to a headband he is wearing. "I think about what I want them to do and they do it."

As Hiro talks, the microbots form a giant hand that waves and then lifts Hiro into the air. The audience applaud excitedly.

Hiro and Tadashi are thrilled to find out that the university wants Hiro to attend the school. Alistair Krei, head of Krei Tech, is impressed by Hiro's microbots and wants to buy them. Hiro follows Professor Callaghan's advice and tells Krei that they're not for sale.

As Hiro and Tadashi leave the showcase a fire breaks
out in the hall. Despite Hiro begging him not to, Tadashi
runs back to help Professor Callaghan, who is still inside!
But there is a huge explosion and neither Tadashi nor
Callaghan ever come back out.

Tadashi's friends try to comfort Hiro, but it's no good.
Hiro just wants to be left alone.

One morning, Hiro hurts his toe. "Ow!"

At Hiro's cry of pain, Baymax inflates to life. Hiro hadn't realized that Tadashi's nurse-bot was still functional.

Baymax scans Hiro so that he can provide the appropriate treatment. But Hiro doesn't want to be treated! As he tries to avoid Baymax, Hiro falls and finds a microbot under his bed.

The microbot buzzes and vibrates. Baymax thinks it looks like it is trying to work out where to go and he wants to use it like a compass and follow it.

Hiro and Baymax are guided to an old warehouse where they see a large machine making microbots.

"My microbots? Why is someone making more?" thinks Hiro, confused. He thought all his microbots had been destroyed in the fire.

Suddenly, the microbots start to move and swarm together. Then a mysterious man in a mask appears behind the microbots and directs them to attack Hiro and Baymax!

Hiro and Baymax manage to escape the warehouse without being hurt, but now Hiro realizes that he needs Baymax to be able to fight and defend him.

He downloads karate moves on to a chip that he loads into the robot. He also creates armour for the nurse-bot to wear.

They return to the warehouse ready to fight! Tadashi's friends also turn up! They are concerned about Hiro and have been following him.

Suddenly, Yokai, the masked man, appears. He is riding on a giant wave of microbots!

The masked villain orders his microbots to attack Hiro and his friends.
The gang try to escape in Wasabi's car, but they are trapped and drive into the bay!

Yokai watches the car sink into the water and leaves, satisfied.

Luckily, Baymax inflates and floats everyone to the surface – they're safe!

Hiro realizes that if they are going to defeat Yokai, then they all need amazing tech.

Back in his garage, Hiro gets to work on upgrading his friends' tech.

He creates discs for Go Go to skate on, which give her super speed, and a portable chemistry lab in Honey's handbag so she can stop a villain with her chem-balls.

Wasabi has gloves that turn into lasers and slice through steel. And comic-loving Fred's Kaiju suit is updated to allow him to super-jump and breathe fire.

Hiro upgrades Baymax with a new super suit that has turbo boots, rocket gloves and wings! Hiro's own super suit has magnets so he can attach himself to Baymax.

As a test, Hiro and Baymax soar over San Fransokyo! Hiro loves it!

"Now, let's go and face the guy who stole my microbots!" Hiro announces.

Hiro has also updated Baymax with an enhanced scanner. Baymax is able to use it to find Yokai, and he directs the gang to a hidden lab.

Inside the lab they discover an old video of Alistair Krei presenting a new teleportation device.

But the test flight went horribly wrong and the pilot, Abigail, was lost inside the whirlpool-like portal!

When the video finishes the team realize that Yokai is behind them.

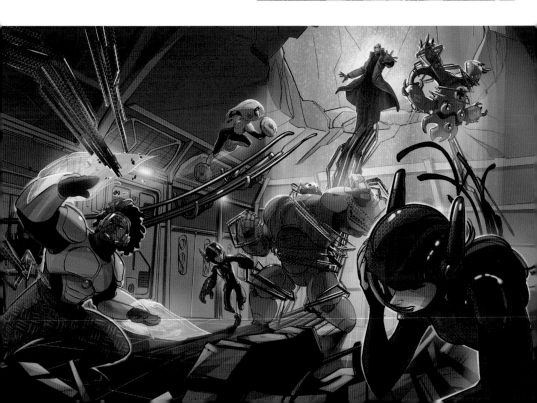

As the friends battle the microbots, Hiro suddenly realizes that Yokai is controlling them with his mask. He rockets towards him on Baymax.

"I know it's you, Krei!" Hiro shouts as he grabs the mask. But it isn't – it is Professor Callaghan!

Hiro can't believe it. He thinks that the professor let Tadashi die in the fire, so he removes Baymax's nursing chip and commands Baymax to attack him. But the rest of the team manage to stop the nurse-bot and replace the chip.

In the meantime, Callaghan escapes with the microbots.

Upset with his friends, Hiro takes Baymax home and tries to remove the nursing chip again.

"Tadashi is here," Baymax says, pointing to his chest. It shows a video of Hiro's brother on the day he activated the nurse-bot.

Hiro finally understands; Tadashi wanted to help people!

Hiro's friends arrive while he
is watching the video.
    The team tell Hiro that they
have worked out that the test
pilot was Callaghan's daughter!
    "This," announces Fred, " is a
revenge story...."

The super team head straight to Krei Tech, where Alistair Krei is giving a speech.

When they get there, they see that Callaghan has used the microbots to build a portal. He wants to destroy Krei and everything that he treasures as revenge for losing his daughter. At Hiro's command, the team leap into action!

The team use their powers and work together to defeat
Callaghan and stop him from destroying everything.

But then Baymax detects signs of life inside the portal and he
and Hiro enter together.

As they fly through, Baymax is badly damaged by debris, but they
find a pilot pod and inside, Abigail!

Baymax is damaged so cannot fly all three of them out of the
portal, so he uses his rocket fist to push Hiro and Abigail to safety.

"Please, no!" cries Hiro. "I need you."
But the boy realizes what he must do to save Abigail.
"I am satisfied with my care," he tells Baymax.

Slowly, things return to normal and Hiro finally starts classes at the university. He misses Tadashi and Baymax, but now he and his friends have a mission: to help others!

One day, Hiro fist bumps Baymax's rocket fist, which reveals a nurse chip clenched inside!
Hiro can rebuild Baymax! He is great at building robots, after all!

Big Hero 6 is a team of crime fighters on their first
ever mission – to save San Fransokyo!
Meet the team and give each one
an overall hero rating out of 10.

Name: Hiro Hamada
Special skill: Robotics
Best invention: Microbots
(tiny robots controlled by your thoughts)
Best weapon: Brain power
Hero score: _____

Name: Baymax
Special skill: Nurse-bot
Best invention: None (Baymax is an
invention, not an inventor)
Best weapon: Rocket fist
Hero score: _____

Name: Honey Lemon
Special skill: Chemistry
Best invention: A chemical that breaks down metal
Best weapon: Chem-balls
Hero score: _____

Name: Go Go Tomago
Special skill: Mechanical Engineering
Best invention: Mag lev frictionless hubs (to make wheels go even faster)
Best weapon: Disc-throwing ability
Hero score: _____

Name: Wasabi
Special skill: Physics
Best invention: A precision optic laser
Best weapon: Plasma blades
Hero score: _____

Name: Fred
Special skill: Comic-book collecting
Best invention: None (Fred is not an inventor or scientist)
Best weapon: Flame thrower
Hero score: _____

SUPERHERO GENIUS

Okay, so your name might not be Hiro Hamada,
but there's a superhero inside every brainiac.
Find yours and fill in your vital stats.

My superhero name is:...

My superhero friends are:..

....

I am ...

☐ a human ☐ a robot

☐ an animal ☐ an alien

☐ something else: ....

My main super power allows me to: ....

....

My other powers include being able to:..

....

....

I wear:...

....

....

My main job is to ...

- ☐ rescue people
- ☐ rescue animals
- ☐ do something else:..
- ☐ save the planet
- ☐ create inventions

My superhero badge or logo looks like this:

FAMILY FIRST

Family comes first for Hiro and his big brother, Tadashi. They live with their Aunt Cass and her cat, Mochi. Read Hiro's family profile and then fill in your own.

Name:
Hiro Hamada

Guardians:
Aunt Cass

Siblings:
One older brother named Tadashi. He's 18.

Family home:
We live above Aunt Cass's café, *The Lucky Cat Café.*

Family pets:
A cat called Mochi (who spends most of the time sleeping).

My role in the family:
Little brother, table wiper, plate clearer. Oh yeah, and robotics wizard!

Name:

....

Guardians:

....

Siblings:

....

....

Family home:

....

....

Family pets:

....

....

My role in the family:

....

....

....

....

Here's a photo or drawing of me in my signature action pose.

BEST BUDS

When Tadashi dies, Baymax becomes Hiro's new best friend and takes good care of him. What do you count on in a best mate?

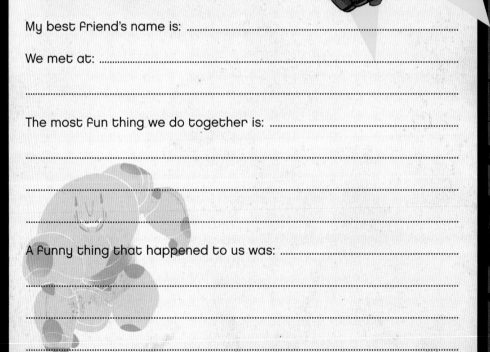

My best friend's name is: ....

We met at: ....

....

The most fun thing we do together is: ....

....

....

A funny thing that happened to us was: ....

....

....

Stick in a photo of one or more of your friends.
Write their names underneath.

In this picture you can see:

....

MY 'BIG 6'

Create your own superhero dream team, choosing five other members. They could be friends, family members or your favourite movie stars. Give them ratings out of 10 for intelligence, strength and speed.

Name:...

Why they should be on my team:

....

....

....

Intelligence: /10

Strength: /10

Speed: /10

Name:...

Why they should be on my team:

....

....

....

Intelligence: /10

Strength: /10

Speed: /10

Name:..

Why they should be on my team:

....

....

....

Intelligence: /10

Strength: /10

Speed: /10

Name:..

Why they should be on my team:

....

....

....

Intelligence: /10

Strength: /10

Speed: /10

Name:..

Why they should be on my team:

....

....

....

Intelligence: /10

Strength: /10

Speed: /10

ワサビ

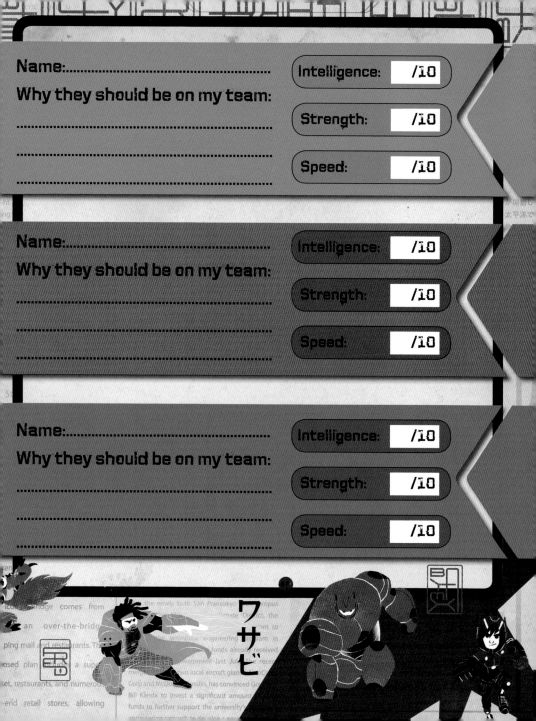

Baymax isn't sure about his new suit of armour — he preferred the huggable look! Rate the new Baymax out of 100 for each skill.

Name: Baymax Mark Two

New features: wings, thrusters, 1000% increased range of sight and rocket fist.

Fighting skills:

Super powers:

Costume:

Team spirit:

ペアマックス

Draw your own robotic invention.
Add labels with arrows to explain what it does.

My invention is called: _____

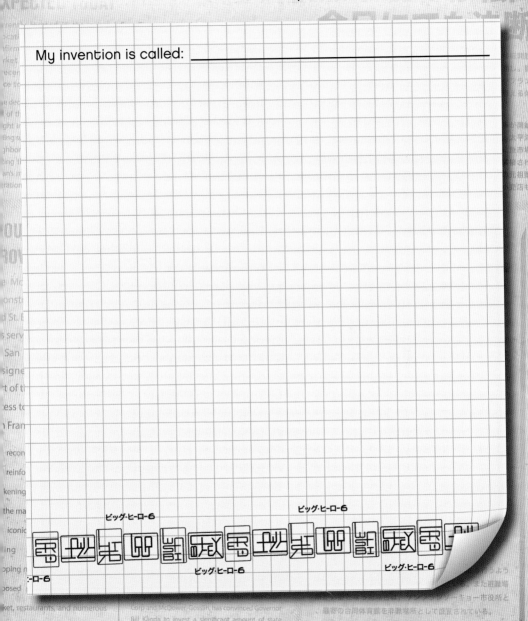

save OUR CITY!

Big Hero 6 is on a mission to save the city from the clutches of the evil Yokai. Imagine a mystery villain is about to strike in your hometown or city. Now plan your mission!

Who's the villain? ....
....

Where is the attack going to take place? ....
....

What's your rescue plan?

....
....
....
....

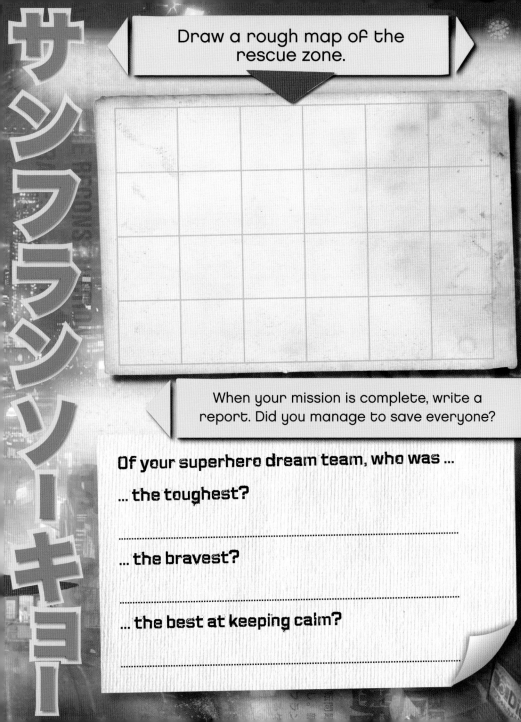

Draw a rough map of the rescue zone.

サンフランシソーキョー

When your mission is complete, write a report. Did you manage to save everyone?

Of your superhero dream team, who was ...

... the toughest?

....

... the bravest?

....

... the best at keeping calm?

....

MICROBOT MAD

Hiro's microbots were all destroyed in a fire ... or so he thinks. Can you design some new ones for him? Remember: microbots are tiny robots that can build things.

ACTION SHOT

The gang is ready for action and Honey is about to take a group selfie. Who's your favourite character?

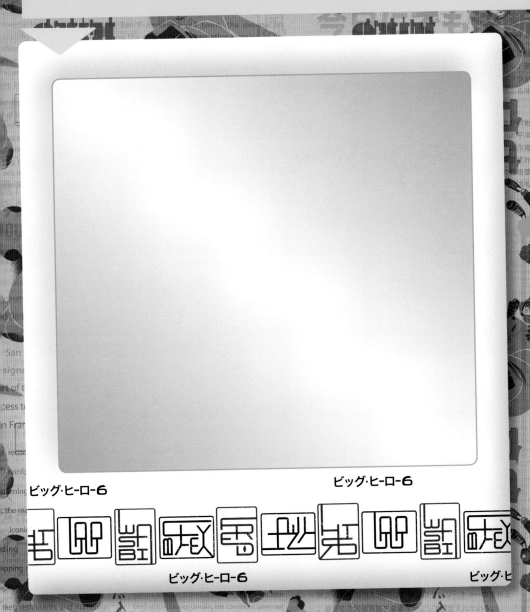

ビッグ・ヒーロ-6

ビッグ・ヒーロ-6

ビッグ・ヒーロ-6

ビッグ・ヒ

CITIZEN SUPERHERO

Tadashi will always be Hiro's number one hero. Who are your heroes? Here's your chance to reward the heroes in your life.

Ultimate hero

Stick photo here

The award goes to:

This person is a hero because:

Hero at school

Stick photo here

The award goes to:

....

This person is a hero because:

....

Hero in the news

Stick photo here

The award goes to:

....

This person is a hero because:

....

Hero in the movies

Stick photo here

The award goes to:

....

This person is a hero because:

....

Hero at home

Stick photo here

The award goes to:

....

This person is a hero because:

....

HERO LOG

Use these pages to write about your superhero acts, real or imaginary. Record a moment when you helped someone, or when you felt proud of yourself.

Something I did for the first time....

Date: ....

What I did:...

....

How I felt: ....

....

Somewhere I went for the first time....

Date: ....

What I did:...

....

....

How I felt: ....

....

Somebody I helped....

Date: ....

What I did:...

....

....

How I felt: ....

....

Something that was fun....

Date: ....

What I did:...

....

....

How I felt: ....

....

ワサビ ヒロ